Modern Dance

Contents

All About Modern Dance 5

What is modern dance?   6

How is modern dance different?   8

The beginnings of modern dance   10

Two famous dancers   12

The future of modern dance   14

A career in modern dance   16

Fiction Story

A Show for Ghana   19

Curtain Call 36

All About Modern Dance

What is modern dance?

Modern dance started at the beginning of the 20th Century.

Some dancers thought that ballet was too limited.

They wanted **more** freedom.

Classical ballet has strict rules:

- about how to dance
- about what to wear.

Some dancers wanted to dance in **different ways.**

They wanted to wear **different costumes.**

They wanted their dancing to show how **they** felt.

This was the start of modern dance.

7

How is modern dance different?

Dance movements

Modern dancers often create their own dance moves.

They don't follow the rules of classical ballet.

Some modern dancers say that any movement is dance.

And any person is a dancer.

Stories

Classical ballet always tells a story.

In modern dance there is often no story. Just feelings.

Costumes

Modern dancers often dance in bare feet.

They wear simple costumes.

The beginnings of modern dance

Isadora Duncan

Some people say that **Isadora Duncan** started modern dance.

She was a dancer, born in 1927 in the USA.

She thought that classical ballet was 'ugly and against nature'.

Her dancing used natural movements and simple costumes. She called it '**free dance**'.

But it shocked many people.

Isadora Duncan was also a **teacher** of dance.

They called her students **The Isadorables**.

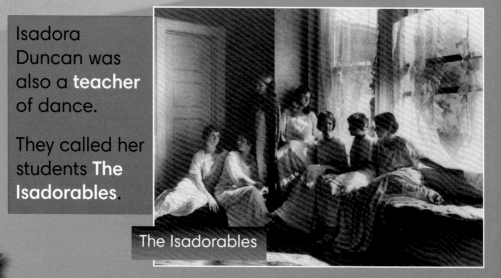
The Isadorables

Martha Graham was a creator of modern dance, too.

She was a brilliant American dancer. She was born in 1894.

Martha Graham and Bertram Ross in 1961.

She invented a **new language** for dance.

Sometimes, she used **sharp** and **jagged** movements.

Martha Graham was a very important **choreographer**, or dance designer.

But she said she really wanted people to remember her as a **dancer**.

Martha Graham dancing in 1937.

Merce Cunningham was a very important American dancer. When he was young he worked with Martha Graham.

Later in his life he was both a dancer and a choreographer.

In 1953 Merce formed his own dance company. He called it the Merce Cunningham Dance Company.

Merce Cunningham worked with many great American musicians and artists. He died in 2009. But his dance company still performs today.

Dancers from the Merce Cunningham Dance Company performing 'Nearly 90' by Merce Cunningham.

Twyla Tharp was born in 1941 in America. She studied with Martha Graham and with Merce Cunningham.

She formed her own dance company in 1965. Her dances often use jazz and pop music. She has written more than 120 dance works.

The future of modern dance

Modern dance is still very young. It was invented less than 100 years ago.

Classical ballet is much older. It is more than 500 years old.

So modern dance is still growing and changing.

In the future, modern dance will be different.

 There will be great new dancers.

 There will be great new choreographers.

Who will be the great dancers of the future?

A career in modern dance

So you want a career in modern dance. What do you do next?

Do you have what it takes?

Do you have talent? If not, you may not succeed.

You need to be very fit.

You also need determination.

Learn and practise

You need to study dance. It's best to study at college.

You need to practise hard, too. Dancers practise for hours every day.

Modern dance or ballet?

Both need the same kinds of skills.

Many ballet dancers do modern dance, too.

If you study both, you will learn more. When you are older, you can decide which to do.

Think about the future

Modern dance is hard work. Many dancers stop performing when they are still quite young.

Think about what you will do after a dance career.

You could be a choreographer. Or a dance teacher.

17

A Show
for Ghana

Chapter One

Dance Aid

Roxy organised modern dance shows. She wanted to put on a show in Ghana, in Africa. The show would raise money for the poor people who lived there.

Roxy met her dance group at the local coffee bar. She told them her idea.

'How are you going to get all the dancers over there?' Callum asked. 'It will cost too much.'

'We can all pay for ourselves to go,' Roxy said.

'You can count me out, then,' said Callum. 'I'm not wasting **my** money.'

The rest of the modern dance group agreed with Callum. It would be a waste of money.

They all left the coffee bar. Only Roxy and her boyfriend Mark were left.

'I'll go with you,' said Mark. 'I think it's a great idea.'

Roxy shook her head. 'We can't put on a show with just the two of us.'

Mark put his hand on Roxy's shoulder. 'Cheer up. We'll find people in Ghana to take part.'

Roxy grinned. 'That's a great idea. The show must go on!'

Chapter Two

Taking part

In Ghana, Jojo was selling jewellery to the tourists in the street. But she was too hot. She fanned her face with her hand. It made no difference.

Jojo moved under a tree to get some shade. Then she saw a poster pinned to the tree. The poster said:

Dancers wanted.
No experience necessary.

'That looks like fun,' thought Jojo. 'I could learn how to dance.'

She decided to go to the meeting to find out more about it.

There were lots of other people at the meeting.

Roxy and Mark told them about the show. There was a buzz of excitement. Everybody wanted to take part.

'Are there any questions?' Roxy asked.

Slowly, Jojo raised her hand. 'What's modern dance?' she asked.

'It's a way of expressing feelings and ideas through dance.' Roxy said.

Jojo frowned. 'I don't understand.'

Chapter Three

Dance yourself dizzy

Mark jumped up. 'Watch me,' he said.

He twisted and twirled across the floor. Everybody watched him. As they watched, one minute they felt sad and the next minute they were smiling.

When he had finished, Jojo and the others cheered.

'That was amazing,' Jojo said. 'I wish I could dance like that.'

'We'll teach you,' said Roxy.

They spent weeks learning the dance moves. Jojo had a great time. She was a good dancer and quickly learned all the moves.

The theatre was booked. The music was sorted. Everything was ready.

But there was one problem.

'We haven't sold any tickets,' Mark told Roxy. 'We'll have to cancel.'

Jojo heard what they said. She didn't want the show to be cancelled. Not after so much work. Anyway, she wanted to dance!

Jojo knew she had to do something to help.

Everything was ready for the show. But there was one problem ...
We haven't sold any tickets. We'll have to cancel!
Oh no! I must do something to help.

Chapter Four

The show must go on

Jojo got everybody together.

'We can't let them cancel the show,' she said.

Everyone agreed. They all went to talk to Mark and Roxy.

'The show must go on,' Jojo told them. 'I am good at selling to tourists. We can sell tickets to the tourists on the streets.'

'That's a great idea,' said Roxy, with a big smile.

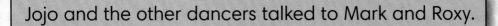

Jojo and the other dancers talked to Mark and Roxy.

We can sell tickets to the tourists.

I can do that!

Great idea!

They all worked hard to sell the tickets. Lots of tourists wanted to see the show.

On the first day of the show, Jojo peeked through the curtains.

'The theatre is packed!' she said.

'All the tickets were sold out,' Roxy said. 'We could never have done all this without you. And you are a really good dancer, as well!'

The show was a big success.

Jojo was especially happy. **This** could be the start of her great new career ...

Curtain Call

ballet

choreographer

choreography

classical ballet

costume

determination

'free dance'

Isadora Duncan

language

Martha Graham

Merce Cunningham

movement

passion

talent

technique

The Isadorables

Twyla Tharp